CW00868417

Contents

OUT OF THE ARK MUSIC

SONG FOR EVERY DAY

1   Songs for every day, help you on your way,
Put the colours back where things are grey.
When you're stuck for words, don't know what to say,
You can sing a song for every day.

> CHORUS *There's a song (so sing it!)*
> *Any time (no limit).*
> *There's a song for each and every day.*
> *There's a song (so sing it!)*
> *Anywhere (just bring it).*
> *Help to make the world a brighter place.*

2   When the sun is up, and the day is new,
When you hear the cock-a-doodle-doo.
If you're feeling down, when there's lots to do,
You can find a song to see you through.

> CHORUS

3   When you're on your own, nothing on your mind,
Sing a simple song to pass the time.
You will be amazed, how the minutes fly,
With a little melody and rhyme.

> CHORUS

4   When you're on the move, walking down the street,
When you feel a rhythm in your feet,
Find yourself a tune, get yourself a beat,
Choose the words to make your song complete.

> LAST CHORUS: *There's a song (so sing it!)*
> *Any time (no limit).*
> *There's a song for each and every day.*
> *There's a song (so sing it!)*
> *Anywhere (just bring it).*
> *Help to make the world a brighter place -*
> *Sing a song for every day.*

SONG FOR EVERY DAY

Words & Music: Mark & Helen Johnson

3

4

MONDAY MORNING

1   Monday morning, time to stop the snoring,
    I must get out of my bed.
    Mum is calling, sounds like it's a warning,
    I'd better do what she says!
       Pull back the bedclothes, over my head goes
       My red pyjama top.
    Take my school-clothes, carefully from the wardrobe,
    Off to the bathroom I pop!

    CHORUS   *It's school today,*
             No time to waste.
             I can't wait to see ev'rybody again.

2   Bathroom's busy, Dad is in a tizzy,
    He can't afford to be late.
    Sister Lizzy's trying to look all pretty,
    Looks like we'll have to wait!
       Mum's in the kitchen, putting out the dishes,
       "Breakfast is on the plate!"
    My clock's ticking, time is going quickly,
    It's nearly quarter past eight.

    CHORUS

3   Put my shoes on, better get a move on,
    Find all my things to take.
    We've not got long, better get my coat on,
    I don't want to be late!

    CHORUS (x 2)
                 I can't wait to see ev'rybody,
                 I can't wait to see ev'rybody,
                 I can't wait to see ev'rybody again!

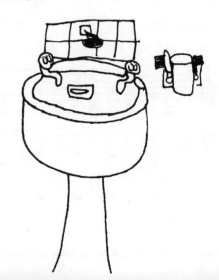

MONDAY MORNING

Words & Music: Mark & Helen Johnson

With enthusiasm ♩ = 137

1. Mon- day mor- ning, time to stop the snor- ing, I must get out of my bed.
2. Bath- room's bus- y, Dad is in a tiz- zy, He can't af- ford to be late.
3. Put my shoes on, bet- er get a move on, Find all my things to take.

Mum is call- ing, sounds like it's a warn- ing, I'd bett- er do what she says!
Sis- ter Liz- zy's try'ng to look all pret- ty, Looks like we'll have to wait!
We've not got long, bet- ter get my coat on, I don't want to be late!

Tick-tone block

Chorus

school to-day no time to waste. I can't wait to see ev'-ry bo- dy a- gain.

(Repeat chorus after v3)

Last time to coda

CODA

I can't wait to

9

PLEASE MISS!

1   Please, Miss - she just took my pencil and I need it.
Why can't she be sensible
I've told her time and time again,
But she says she won't be my friend!

2   Please, Miss - he just called me names and said I'm stupid.
He is such a pain you know
I've heard it time and time again,
It really drives me round the bend!

3   Please, Miss - somebody has stolen my PE kit,
This one here has holes in 'cause
They've worn it time and time again,
I can't wear <u>this</u>, it needs a mend.

    CHORUS *In case you think I'm being nasty,*
I thought you really ought to know.
I'm telling you to save you asking -
Just turn around and look at that, I TOLD YOU SO!

4   Please, Miss - so and so is being such a fidget!
I know she doesn't mean it but
She fusses time and time again,
I really wish she'd move away.

5   Please, Miss - someone's torn my picture and they've spoilt it.
It really makes me sick, I've had to
Start it time and time again,
Now all that work has been in vain.

    CHORUS

6   (TEACHER)
Dismissed! - I've had quite enough of all this business!
All I ever hear about is
"He did this" and "She did that" -
Tittle tattle, yak, yak, yak! (Repeat last 2 lines)

PLEASE MISS!

Words & Music: Mark & Helen Johnson

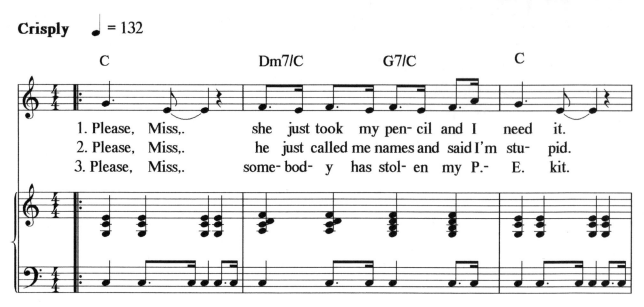

1. Please, Miss,. she just took my pen- cil and I need it.
2. Please, Miss,. he just called me names and said I'm stu- pid.
3. Please, Miss,. some- bod- y has stol- en my P.- E. kit.

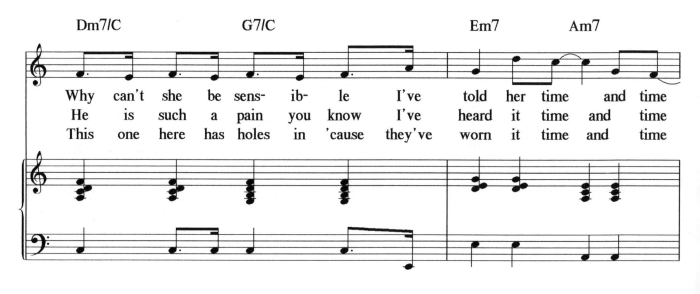

Why can't she be sens- ib- le I've told her time and time
He is such a pain you know I've heard it time and time
This one here has holes in 'cause they've worn it time and time

(v6 to Coda)

ag- ain, but she says she won't be my friend!
ag- ain, it real- ly drives me round the bend!
ag- ain, I can't wear this it needs a mend!

Chorus

In case you think I'm be- ing nast- y,

I thought you real- ly ought to know.

I'm tell- ing you to save you

14

4   Please, Miss - so and so is being such a fidget!
     I know she doesn't mean it but
     She fusses time and time again,
     I really wish she'd move away.

5   Please, Miss - someone's torn my picture and they've spoilt it.
     It really makes me sick, I've had to
     Start it time and time again,
     Now all that work has been in vain.

     CHORUS

6   (TEACHER)
     Dismissed! - I've had quite enough of all this business!
     All I ever hear about is
     "He did this" and "She did that" -
     Tittle tattle, yak, yak, yak! (Repeat last 2 lines)

JUST THE SAME

1   You may be happy you may be sad
You may be pretty or plain.
You may be skinny or getting fat
- Maybe you wish you could change.

2   You may be wealthy you may be poor
You may be scruffy or smart.
But love is real when you know for sure
It takes you just as you are.

    CHORUS *If we're right or we're wrong*
If we're weak or we're strong.
If we're winning or losing a game
Whether black or white skin
With a frown or a grin
Well the Lord loves us all just the same.

3   They say to copy the TV stars
They say "Keep up with the trends".
To have the fashions and look the part
Just like the rest of your friends.

4   They say "Try harder", they say "Perform"
They say "Do things to impress".
But love is real when you know for sure
It won't depend on success ....

    CHORUS (x 2)

JUST THE SAME

Words & Music: Mark & Helen Johnson

17

3 They say to copy the TV stars
  They say "Keep up with the trends".
  To have the fashions and look the part
  Just like the rest of your friends.

4 They say "Try harder", they say "Perform"
  They say "Do things to impress".
  But love is real when you know for sure
  It won't depend on success ....

CHORUS (x 2)

LUNCHTIME QUEUE

1   Down in my tummy, I'm feeling so hungry,
My mind is on nothing but lovely food.
When you've not eaten for hours at least then
You can't help but dream in the lunchtime queue.

    CHORUS *What's on the menu for lunchtime today?*
                Let me imagine what it might say:

2   Egg-burger, cheese-burger, barbecued bean-burger,
Guaranteed lean, served with french fries too.
Tagliatelli, with cheese that is smelly,
To fill up my belly, all afternoon.

    CHORUS

3   Jacket potato with salad that tastes so
Delicious with mayo and good for you.
Savoury pizza with my favourite meatza
So tasty to eat when you're in the mood.

    CHORUS

4   Pineapple fritters with banana splitters and
Raspberry ripple served with a spoon.
Strawberry shortcakes with cream, like my mum makes,
And thick chocolate milkshakes, would nicely do.

    CHORUS

5   GROUP ONE: Repeats verse 1

    GROUP TWO: I'll tell you what's on the menu -
                      It's cottage pie or stew.
                      Cook has been busy all morning.
                      Her food will have to do!

LUNCHTIME QUEUE

Words & Music: Mark & Helen Johnson

With a lilt ♩ = 110

1. Down in my tum- my I'm feel- ing so hun- gry, my
2. Egg- burg- er, cheese- burg- er, bar- be- cued bean- burg- er,
3. Jack- et po- ta- to with sal- ad that tastes so del-
4. Pine- app- le frit- ters with ban- an- a split- ters and

mind is on noth- ing but love- ly food.
guar- an- teed lean, served with french fries too.
ic- ious with may- o and good for you.
rasp- ber- ry rip- ple served with a spoon.

When you've not eat- en for hou- rs at least then you
Tag- li- a- tel- li with cheese that is smel- ly, to
Sav- our- y piz- za with my fav- 'rite meat- za, so
Straw- ber- ry short- cakes with cream, like my mum makes, and

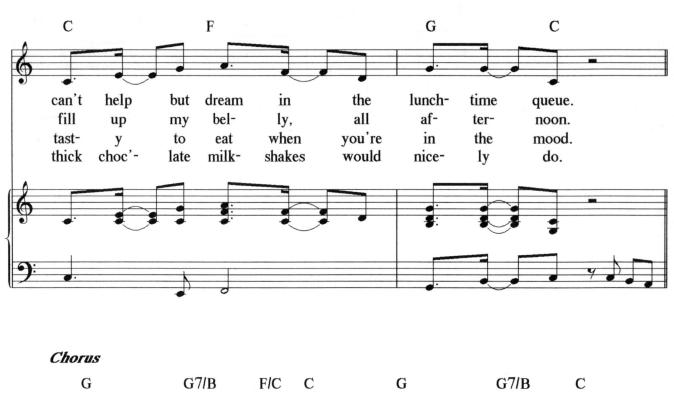

can't help but dream in the lunch- time queue.
fill up my bel- ly, all af- ter- noon.
tast- y to eat when you're in the mood.
thick choc'- late milk- shakes would nice- ly do.

Chorus

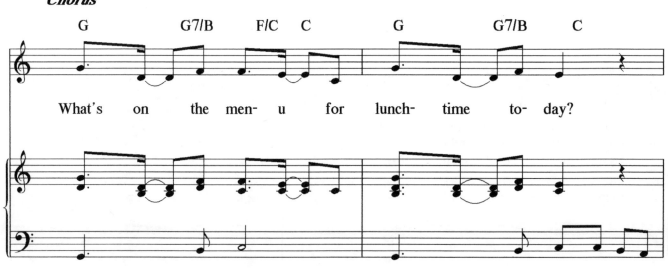

What's on the men- u for lunch- time to- day?

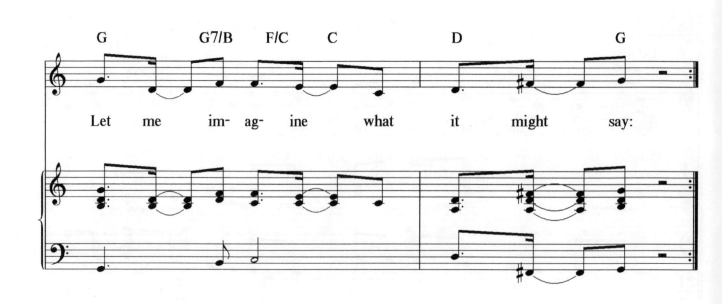

Let me im- ag- ine what it might say:

[A] 5. I'll tell you what's on the men- u,

[B] Down in my tum- my I'm feel- ing so hung- ry my

It's cott- age pie or stew.

mind is on noth- ing but love- ly food.

Cook has been bus- y all morn- ing,

When you've not eat- en for hou- rs at least then you

23

A TIME FOR EVERYTHING

There's a time to laugh, there's a time to cry,
A time to ask the question "Why?".
There's a time for birth, when you say "Hello",
A time to turn and wave goodbye.
There's a time to reap, and a time to sow,
A time to wait and watch things grow.
- There's a time for everything,
It's all a part of life.

There's a time to work, there's a time to play,
A time to learn in every day.
There's a time to build, and a time to mend,
And there's a time to throw away,
There's a time to find, and a time to lose,
And there's a time for you to choose.
- There's a time for everything,
It's all a part of life.

There's a time to shout, there's a time to talk,
And there's a time for simple thoughts.
There's a time to rush, there's a time to stop,
And there's a time for gentle walks.
There's a time to do, and a time to dream,
A time to doubt and to believe.
- There's a time for everything,
It's all a part of life.

TIME FOR EVERYTHING

Words & Music: Mark & Helen Johnson

1. There's a time to laugh, there's a time to cry, a time to
2. There's a time to work, there's a time to play, a time to
3. There's a time to shout, there's a time to talk, and there's a

ask the ques- tion "Why?". There's a time for birth, when you say "Hel- lo",
learn in ev'- ry day. There's a time to build, and a time to mend,
time for sim- ple thoughts. There's a time to rush, there's a time to stop,

C   F   F7

a time to turn and wave good- bye. There's a time to reap,
and there's a time to throw a- way. There's a time to find,
and there's a time for gen- tle walks. There's a time to do,

B♭   C   F

and a time to sow, a time to wait and watch things grow,
and a time to lose, and there's a time for you to choose.
and a time to dream, a time to doubt and to bel- ieve,

D   B♭ /G   Dm/A B♭ B♭/C

There's a time for ev'- ry- thing, it's all a part of
There's a time for ev'- ry- thing, it's all a part of
There's a time for ev'- ry- thing, it's all a part of

27

GREEN SONG

1   People will you hear the warning?
Energy supplies are falling
Every day we're using more and more.
Creatures of the living kingdom
Are in danger of extinction
Something for us all to think on now!

2   Have you heard of global warming?
Did you know the poles are thawing?
Can't afford to just ignore it now.
Let's be under no illusion
Acid rain and air pollution
Need some practical solutions now.

3   What will be our explanation
To our future generations?
Let's assemble all the nations now.
Who can say just what'll happen
If we don't take any action?
We must start a chain reaction now.

4   Governments and politicians
Now's the time for you to listen!
What we need are good decisions now.
Let's look after the planet
God's the one who began it
Time for saving the land is now!

(Repeat last line)

THE GREEN SONG

Words & Music: Mark & Helen Johnson

1. Peo-ple will you hear the war-ning? En-er-gy supp-lies are fall-ing,
4. Gov-ern-ments and pol-i-tic-ians, now's the time for you to list-en!

ev'-ry day we're us-ing more and more.
What we need are good de-cis-ions now.

Creat-ures of the liv-ing king-dom are in dan-ger of ex-tinc-tion,
Let's look af-ter the plan-et, God's the one who be-gan it,

Let's be un- der no ill- us- ion, ac- id rain and air poll- ut- ion,

need some prac- ti- cal sol- ut- ions now!

3. What will be our ex- plan- at- ion, to our fu- ture gen- er- at- ions?

GOOD THINGS

1   Baking bread, country air,
Freshly laundered clothes to wear,
Tidy lawns, roses fair,
Smell so good to me.

2   Tender hands, silky sheets,
Gentle sand beneath my feet,
Soothing baths, summer breeze,
Feel so good to me.

CHORUS   *There are so many good things for us*
To appreciate.
Ev'rybody join in the chorus
We can celebrate!
(Repeat)

3   Cloudless skies, mountain views,
When somebody smiles at you,
A page of ticks, plate of food
Look so good to me.

4   Juicy fruit - good to eat,
Bars of chocolate, bags of sweets,
Fizzy drinks in the heat
Taste so good to me.

CHORUS

5   Singing birds, warm "Hellos",
Music on the radio,
Loud guitars, saxophones
Sound so good to me.

LAST TIME CHORUS

There are so many good things for us
To appreciate.
Ev'rybody join in the chorus
We can celebrate.

There are so many good things for us
To appreciate.
Thank the Lord for his loving kindness
Each and ev'ry day!

GOOD THINGS

Words & Music: Mark & Helen Johnson

1. Bak- ing bread, count- ry air, fresh- ly laund- ered clothes to - wear. Ti- dy lawns, ro- ses fair,
2. Ten- der hands, sil- ky sheets, gen- tle sand be- neath my - feet. Sooth- ing baths, summ- er breeze,

Shaker

35

F#m7   B6   E   1.   2.

We   can   cel-   eb-   rate!   -rate!
each   and   ev'-   ry   day!   day!

v1-4 *D.C.*

v1-4 *D.C.*

3   Cloudless skies, mountain views,
      When somebody smiles at you,
      A page of ticks, a plate of food
      Look so good to me.

4   Juicy fruit - good to eat,
      Bars of chocolate, bags of sweets,
      Drinks and ice cream in the heat
      Taste so good to me.

      CHORUS

5   Singing birds, warm "Hellos",
      Music on the radio,
      Loud guitars and saxophones
      Sound so good to me.

      LAST TIME CHORUS

                There are so many good things for us
                To appreciate.
                Ev'rybody join in the chorus
                We can celebrate.

                There are so many good things for us
                To appreciate.
                Thank the Lord for his loving kindness
                Each and ev'ry day!

ON THE MOVE

1   I like riding in a train,
Jumping on a bus, flying in a plane.
I like doing it again,
'Cause I'm always on the move.
I like floating on a raft,
Diving in a sub, sailing with a mast,
      There are many ways to choose,
      When you're going on the move.

    CHORUS *No matter where I'm heading,*
                  However I may go,
                  I've got to say the best thing
                  Will be the journey home.

2   I like climbing up a rope,
Swinging from a tree, sliding down a slope.
I like going in a boat,
'Cause I'm always on the move.
I like speeding on my skates,
Racing on my bike, slamming on the brakes,
      There are many ways to choose,
      When you're going on the move.

    CHORUS

3   I like gliding off a cliff,
Riding on the waves, swimming like a fish.
I like cruising in a ship,
'Cause I'm always on the move.
I like being in a car,
Sitting on a coach, moving very fast,
      There are many ways to choose,
      When you're going on the move.

ON THE MOVE

Words & Music: Mark & Helen Johnson

1. I like riding in a train, jumping on a bus, flying in a plane. I like doing it again, 'cause I'm always on the

2. I like climbing up a rope, swinging from a tree, sliding down a slope. I like going in a boat, 'cause I'm always on the

3. I like gliding off a cliff, riding on the waves, swimming like a fish. I like cruising in a ship, 'cause I'm always on the

40

41

THE "LOSING THINGS" SONG

1   Tell me why I'm always losing everything,
First my school tie, now my violin.
Boy, will I be for it, when my dad comes in!
I can't explain, how I've mislaid, my precious violin.

        CHORUS *I've looked behind the sofa,*
I've checked beneath the stairs.
I've emptied out the cupboards
And still it isn't there.
I've searched the house all over and
I'm tearing out my hair, 'cause
I can't find my (fiddle/vest/homework) anywhere!

2   Just the other morning, I was getting dressed,
Could I find my polyester vest?!
When I told my mum she wasn't too impressed.
I can't explain, how I've mislaid, my polyester vest.

    CHORUS

3   Sitting in the classroom, working at my desk,
Teacher asks for homework that was set.
Have I got a problem? Yes, my face <u>is</u> red.
I can't explain, how I've mislaid, the homework that was set.

    CHORUS

4   Have you ever noticed, things develop legs?
Here one minute, disappeared the next!
When at last I find them, I'll tie them round my neck,
My violin, my homework and my polyester vest!!

THE "LOSING THINGS" SONG

Words & Music: Mark & Helen Johnson

43

1,2,3.

I can't ex- plain, how I've mis- laid, my prec- ious vi- o- lin. I've
I can't ex- plain, how I've mis- laid, my pol- y- es- ter vest.
I can't ex- plain, how I've mis- laid, the home- work that was set.

Chorus

looked be- hind the so- fa, I've checked be- neath the stairs, I've

em- ptied out the cup- boards, and still it is- n't there. I've

searched the house all ov- er and I'm tear- ing out my hair, 'cause

I can't find my fid- dle
vest- an- y- where!
home- work

4.

my vi- o- lin, my

home- work and my pol- y- es- ter vest!!

NEWSPAPER PICTURES

1   Hollow faces of famine and fear,
Children dying each day.
Mothers silently love through the tears
As life just fades away.

2   Tanks roll into a war shattered town,
Its buildings-blackened remains.
Wounded bodies lie scattered around
And lives are blown away.

    CHORUS   *Newspaper pictures that stare from the page,*
Tell of a world filled with pain.
Can we imagine just how it must be
When colour turns to grey -
When colour turns to grey?

3   Cardboard blankets and old paper sheets
Homes that soak up the rain,
Fragile houses that litter the streets
With lives just thrown away.

4   Trees and buildings are torn from the ground,
As families watch in dismay.
Floods and hurricanes plunder the land
As hopes are washed away.

    CHORUS

5   A father sits with his head in his hands,
He sees a world gone astray.
He wonders when will we all understand,
When will we find the way?

    CHORUS

NEWSPAPER PICTURES

Words & Music: Mark & Helen Johnson

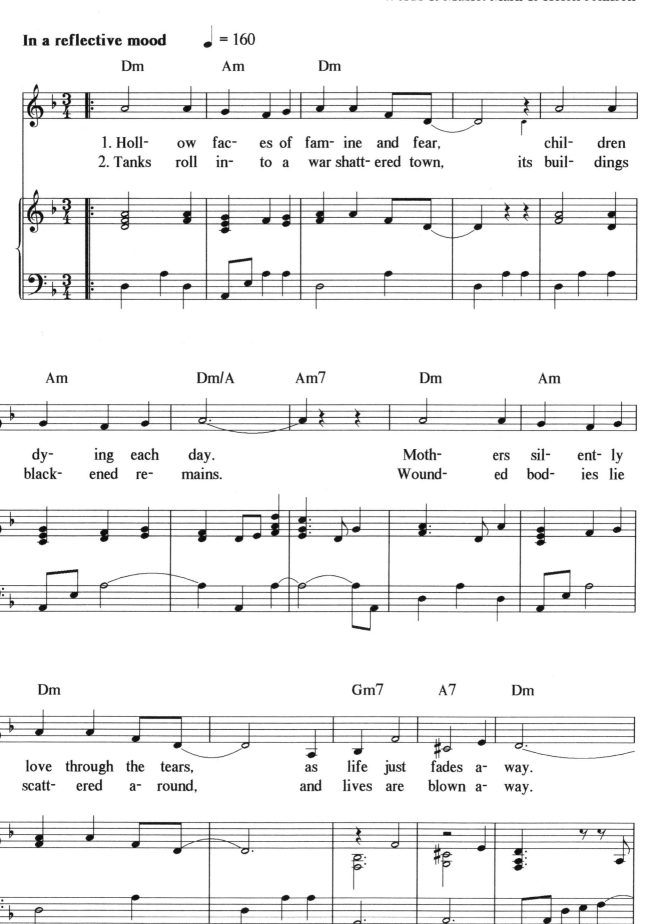

47

Chorus

News- pap- er pic- tures that stare from the page, tell of a world filled with pain.

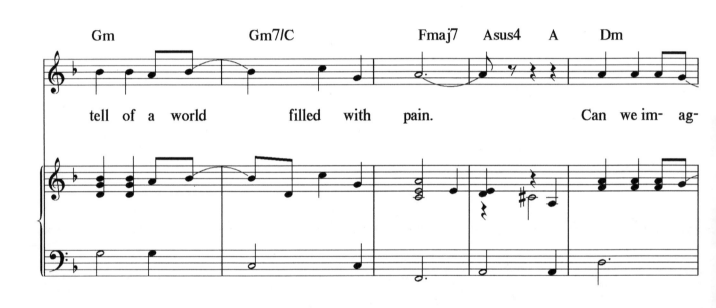

Can we im-ag-ine just how it must be, when col- our turns to

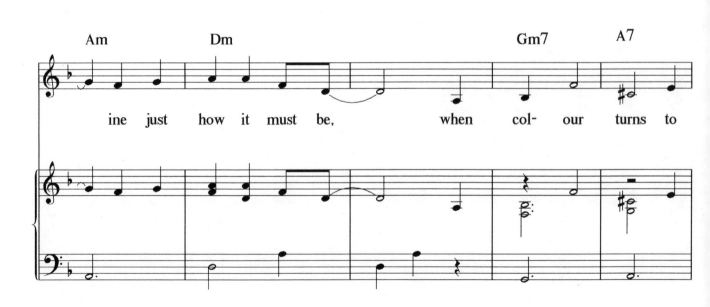

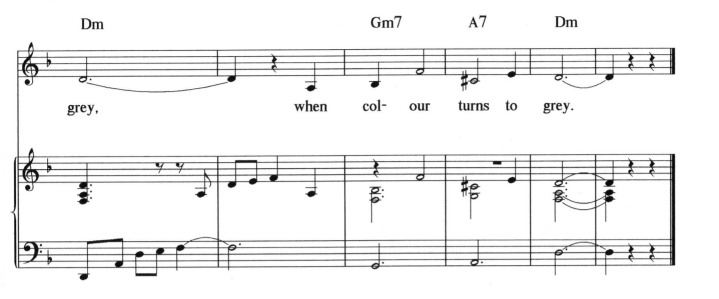

grey,   when col- our turns to grey.

3   Cardboard blankets and old paper sheets
     Homes that soak up the rain,
     Fragile houses that litter the streets
     With lives just thrown away.

4   Trees and buildings are torn from the ground,
     As families watch in dismay.
     Floods and hurricanes plunder the land
     As hopes are washed away.

     CHORUS

5   A father sits with his head in his hands,
     He sees a world gone astray.
     He wonders when will we all understand,
     When will we find the way?

     CHORUS

SEVEN DAYS A WEEK

Monday — We'll have fun day
Tuesday — Hear the news day
Wednesday — See some friends day

Half way through the week.

Thursday — 'Ums and 'ers day
Friday — Punch the sky day
Saturday — It won't matter day

Nearly through the week.

CHORUS *When Sunday comes*
We can have a little rest for one day
The work is done
And the day is free.
Take time to ponder on all the things
You've said and done day
And thank the Lord for another week!

12|24
Track 15430

7 DAYS A WEEK

Words & Music: Mark & Helen Johnson

With a rock feel ♩ = 150

Mon-day, we'll have fun day, Tues-day, hear the news day, Wedn's-day, see some friends day, half-way through the week. Thurs-day, ums and ers day, Fri-

day,   punch   the sky day, Sat- ur-day,   it   won't matt- er day,

Last time to coda *Chorus*

near-ly through   the week.   When Sun-day   comes we can have a lit-tle

rest for one   day.   The work is   done and the day is   free.

GOD CREATED THEM ALL

1   Sun and moon and the star-lit sky,
       God created them all.
     Rivers and seas and the oceans wide,
       He created them all.
     Forests and fields and the deserts dry,
       God created them all.
     Valleys and foothills and mountains high,
       He created them all.

     CHORUS *God looked down from heaven,*
                 He was pleased, ... o yeah.
                 Everything was just as it should be, ... ah ha.

2   Ev-er-y creature that moves and breathes,
       God created them all.
     Fliers and swimmers and some with feet,
       He created them all.
     Beautiful flowers and fruitful trees,
       God created them all.
     Ev-er-y plant that you'll ever see,
       He created them all.

     CHORUS

3   Summer and Autumn, and Winter and Spring,
       God created them all.
     Each of the changes the seasons bring,
       He created them all.
     Thunder and lightning, the rain and wind,
       God created them all.
     Glorious sunsets and snowy scenes,
       He created them all.

     CHORUS

     LAST TIME: *God created the whole wide world,*
                  He created it all!

GOD CREATED THEM ALL

Words & Music: Mark & Helen Johnson

1. Sun and the moon and the star- lit sky,
2. Ev- er- y crea- ture that moves and breathes,
3. Sum- mer and Aut- umn and Win- ter, Spring,

God cre- at- ed them all.
God cre- at- ed them all.
God cre- at- ed them all.

Riv- ers and seas and the
Fli- ers and swimm- ers and
Each of the chang- es the

oc- eans wide, He cre- at- ed them all.
some with feet, He cre- at- ed them all.
seas- ons bring, He cre- at- ed them all.

Forests and fields and the deserts dry, God cre- at- ed them all.
Beau- ti- ful flow- ers and fruit- ful trees, God cre- at- ed them all.
Thun- der and light- ning, the rain and wind, God cre- at- ed them all.

Vall- eys and foot- hills and moun- tains high,
Ev- er- y plant that you'll ev- er see,
Glor- i- ous sun- sets and snow- y scenes,

He cre- at- ed them all.
He cre- at- ed them all.
He cre- at- ed them all.

Chorus

God looked down from

Claves

57

HAPPY BIRTHDAY

Happy Birthday, Happy Birthday,
Happy Birthday, once again.
It's time to wish you Happy Birthday,
Time to sing a birthday song.
You're 365 days older now than you were last year,
365 days older now.

1   Happy Birthday, Happy Birthday,
      Happy Birthday once again.

2   It's time to wish you Happy Birthday,
      Time to sing a birthday song.

3   You're three hundred and sixty five days older
         now than you were last year.
      Three hundred and sixty five days older now.

Last time
Happy Birthday, Happy Birthday,
Happy Birthday once again.

HAPPY BIRTHDAY

Words & Music: Mark & Helen Johnson

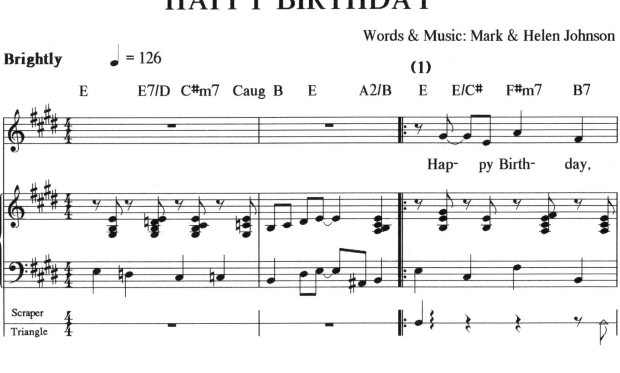

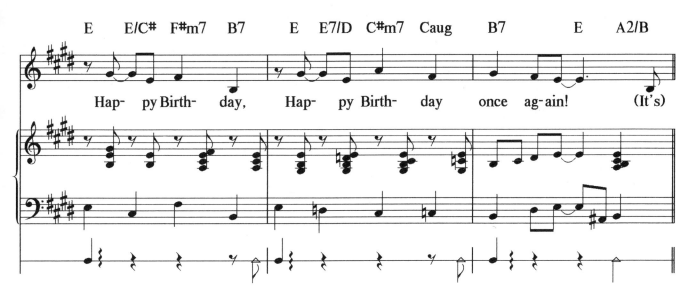

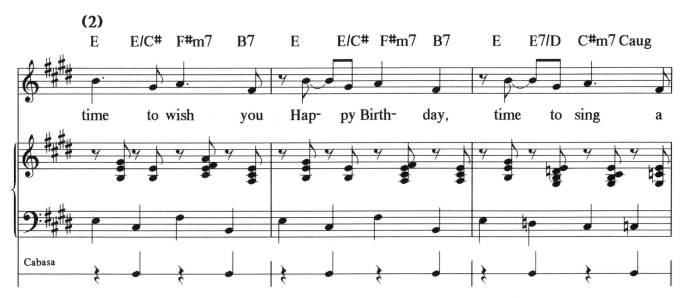

59

(3)

Birth- day song. (You're) three hun- dred and six- ty five days

old- er now than you were last year, three hun- dred and six- ty five days

ol - der now!

Bell tree

60

TAKING MY TIME

1   Have you ever ..... stopped to question why we're
    All so busy rushing around?
    I would rather ..... start a fashion for a
    Life that's bright and breezy,
    By taking my time ..... taking my time.

2   City people ..... pushing quickly through the
    Streets and stations, traffic and crowds.
    Rushing past me ..... no-one asks me but I'll
    Reach my destination
    By taking my time ..... taking my time.

    CHORUS *People always tell me they're in a rush,*
            They mustn't stop for long.
            I can only say that they miss so much -
            Slow things down and start to have fun!

3   Fast food places ..... where the pace is geared to
    Filling faces, fast as you can.
    Hungry people ..... queue for tables, but I'm
    Going to keep them waiting
    By taking my time ..... taking my time.

4   Hasty shoppers ..... with their trollies full of
    Special offers, chase me around.
    I'm avoiding ..... playing dodgems down the
    Aisles and past the freezers
    By taking my time ..... taking my time.

    CHORUS

5   Repeat verse 1

    ..... taking my time ..... taking my time .....
    ..... I've made up my mind ..... I'm taking my time .....
    (Repeat and fade)

TAKING MY TIME

Words & Music: Mark & Helen Johnson

start a fash- ion for a life that's bright and bree-
no- one asks me, but I'll reach my des- tin- a-
queue for tab- les but I'm going to keep them wait-
play- ing dod- gems down the aisles and past the freez-

Last time to coda

zy by tak-ing my time,.. tak-ing my time.
tion by tak-ing my time,.. tak-ing my time.
ing by tak-ing my time,.. tak-ing my time.
ers by tak-ing my time. tak-ing my time.

Chorus

Peo- ple al- ways tell me they're in a rush, they

Triangle

63

must- n't stop for long. I can on- ly say that they

miss so much. Slow things down and start to have fun.

(to v3)
(repeat v1)

CODA

tak- ing my time.

Repeat and fade